MINION LANGUAGE

An essential part of being a Minion is knowing how to talk like a Minion. Can you fill the missing letters into these essential Minion phrases?

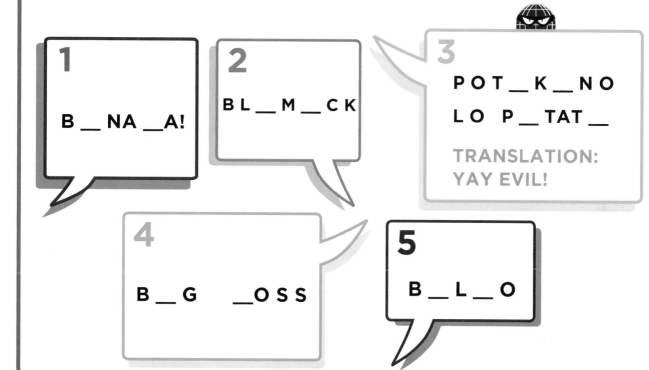

1

B _ NA _ _A!

2

B L _ _ M _ _ C K

3

P O T _ _ K _ _ N O
L O P _ _ T A T _ _

TRANSLATION:
YAY EVIL!

4

B _ _ G   _ _ O S S

5

B _ _ L _ _ O

Now design a unique logo for the front of your overalls. This will make the tribe stand out from all the other henchmen out there.

HOW DID YOU DO?
Check your answers
on page 55.

Masters through history: T. rex

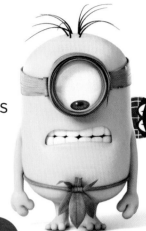

**Minions only have one aim in life –
to serve the most despicable master around.**

And after following evil amoebae, fish and amphibians for millennia, the next big step was, of course, T. rex!

MASTER PROS:

- T. rex was mean
- Great ROAR
- Also doubles as mode of transport

MASTER FAIL:

- T. rex was vulnerable to death when he fell into a volcano!

DID YOU KNOW?
- T. rex's name means **tyrant lizard**.
- T. rex lived 70 million years ago.
- T. rex was 12m long. That's about the same length as a bus!

Wrong Rex

It's so hard keeping hold of a master.

Can you spot ten differences between these two photos of when it all went wrong for T. rex?

HOW DID YOU DO? Check your answers on page 55.

5

MASTERS THROUGH HISTORY: CAVEMAN

When Minions met man they knew they were onto a good thing.

Although man was shorter and hairier than T. rex, he was much smarter. Unfortunately, early man was apparently quite delicious.

MASTER PROS:

- Stylish use of fur clothing!
- Fun tools
- Complimentary cave

MASTER FAIL:

- Bears think cavemen are very tasty!

DID YOU KNOW?

- Early humans and us are all part of the same family called Homo sapiens.
- *Homo sapien* means **knowing man**.

SQUIGGLY LINE OF DESTINY

Minions may all look the same, but they're actually quite unique.

For example, these three Minions are all in search of something different.

Follow the paths and find out what each one is looking for – and who will be surprised by a bear!

HOW DID YOU DO?
Check your answers
on page 55.

7

MASTERS THROUGH HISTORY: PHARAOH

The tribes' search for a despicable master continued through the ages, until they came to the Egyptians. Here was a society obsessed with worshipping their masters – perfect!

MASTER PROS:

- Lives in warm climate
- Fun and challenging building projects
- Cool outfits

MASTER FAIL:

- Pharaohs are easily squished by Minion made monuments!

DID YOU KNOW?
- Pharaoh was the name given to a king or queen of ancient Egypt.
- Most Ancient Egyptian pyramids were built as tombs for pharaohs.
- Both Egyptian men and women wore makeup.

HIEROGLYPHIC HIJINKS

Who's been drawing on the walls again? Oh wait, that's a Minion hieroglyphic pattern.

Can you complete each row? Use your stickers to add the next Minion in the sequences.

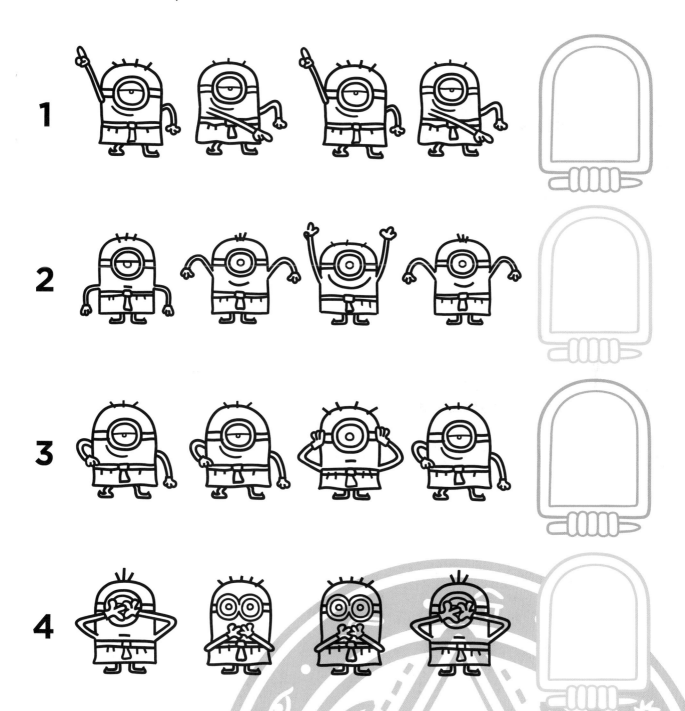

HOW DID YOU DO?
Check your answers on page 55.

9

MASTERS THROUGH HISTORY:
DRACULA

The Minions loved working for Dracula.

He partied all night and slept all day. The Minions knew Dracula loved parties so much that they decided to throw him a special bash for his 357th birthday.

MASTER PROS:

- Mean AND spooky
- Sweet cape
- No cooking required

MASTER FAIL:

- Dracula turns to dust when exposed to sunlight – oops!

DID YOU KNOW?
- Dracula means son of the dragon.
- Vampires like to sleep all day and party all night.
- Vampires cannot be exposed to sunlight.

BIRTHDAY BLOOPER

Dracula's 357th birthday didn't quite go as planned!

Find the missing jigsaw piece stickers to show what went wrong and complete the picture.

WHAT A PAIN IN THE NECK!

One of the pieces is wrong. Use your pens to finish the picture instead.

HOW DID YOU DO?
Check your answer on page 55.

MASTERS THROUGH HISTORY: PIRATE

Minions were happy to serve their Pirate master.

It meant sailing, piles of plunder, great outfits, cool songs and a language that was just as incomprehensible as their own!

But before long it was the same sad story . . .

Master Pros:

- Life at sea!
- No showers required
- Cool catchphrases

Master fail:

- Pirates are just the right size to be shark bait!

DID YOU KNOW?

- Pirates had many superstitions and believed that piercing their ears would improve their eyesight.
- Most pirating happened between 1690 and 1720.
- Pirates used compasses to navigate.

SCARLET OVERKILL FACT FILE

MOVE ASIDE, MEN. THERE'S A NEW BAD MAN IN TOWN AND THAT MAN IS A WOMAN!

FACT FILE

NAME: Scarlet Overkill

APPEARANCE: Impeccably stylish! 1960s beehive hairdo, red dress, long black gloves

LOVES: Herb, her trophies from various crimes, the English Royal Family (especially their jewels!)

HATES: When her henchmen fail her and when people betray her.

MOST EVIL MOMENT: Overthrowing the Queen and inviting all of the villains to England.

MOST LIKELY TO SAY:

"DOESN'T IT FEEL SO GOOD TO BE BAD?"

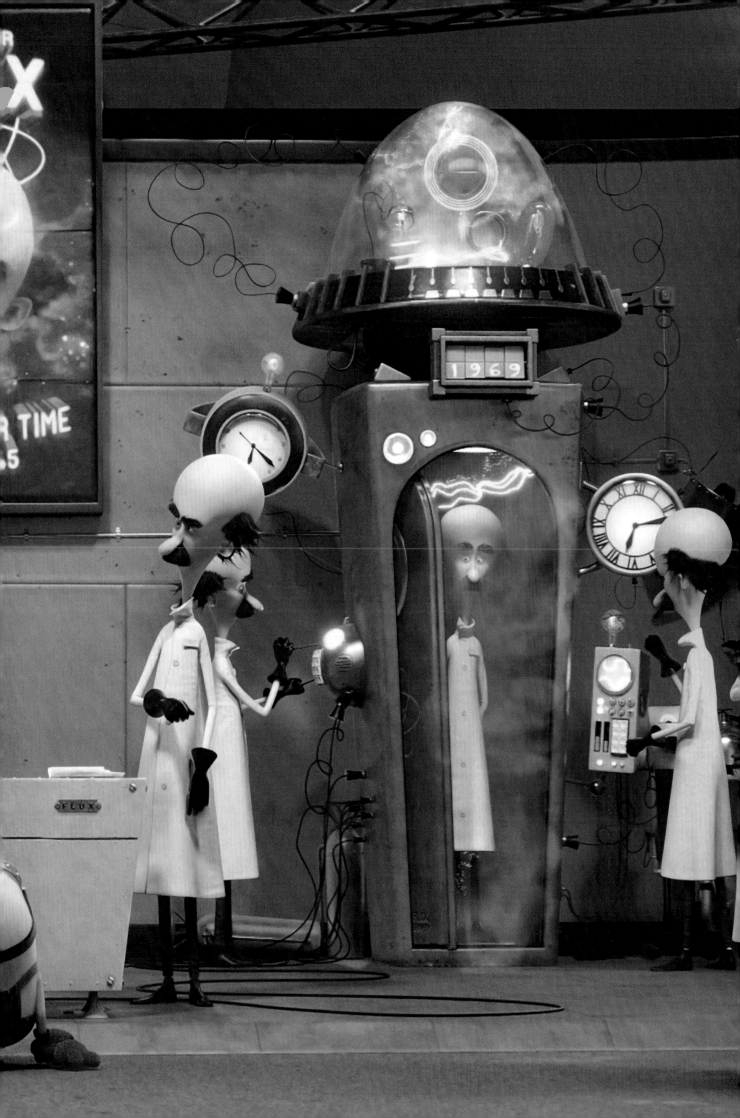

HERB OVERKILL FACT FILE

He's a super-genius inventor and the husband of Scarlet Overkill. He's cool, he's hip and he's crazy (in love with Scarlet)!

FACT FILE

NAME: Herb Overkill

APPEARANCE: Cool hair, cool suit – he's simply cool.

LOVES: His super villain wife Scarlet, inventing gadgetry, soup (especially depicted in paintings), romance, explosions

FUNNIEST/MOST EVIL MOMENT: Taking selfies with vintage torture devices

MOST LIKELY TO SAY:

"IT'S UNBELIEVABLE, **BUT** BELIEVE IT!"

Page 2

USE THESE STICKERS ON THE ACTIVITY PAGES:

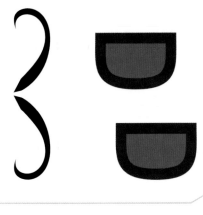

Page 9

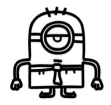

Page 11

Page 20

VILLAIN-CON

For 89 years the biggest gathering of criminals from around the globe. Brought to you by the **Villain Network Channel**

– "IF YOU TELL ANYONE, WE'LL FIND YOU!"

THERE'S SO MUCH TO DO, IT'S CRIMINAL:

ATTEND GUEST LECTURES FROM ESTEEMED VILLAINS.

MAKE CONTACTS IN THE UNDERWORLD COMMUNITY.

LEARN YOUR CRIMINAL TRADE.

SAMPLE THE NEWEST IN VILLAIN TECHNOLOGY.

MEET YOUR IDOLS AND EVEN FIND YOUR DREAM JOB.

AND FOR THE FIRST TIME ANYWHERE: A SPECIAL APPEARANCE FROM THE FIRST FEMALE SUPER VILLAIN, SCARLET OVERKILL!

DO YOU HAVE WHAT IT TAKES?
FIND OUT!

Industry professionals will be on-hand throughout the convention to offer critique and review your villainous skills. Ask a professional to help you on the next step of your criminal career!

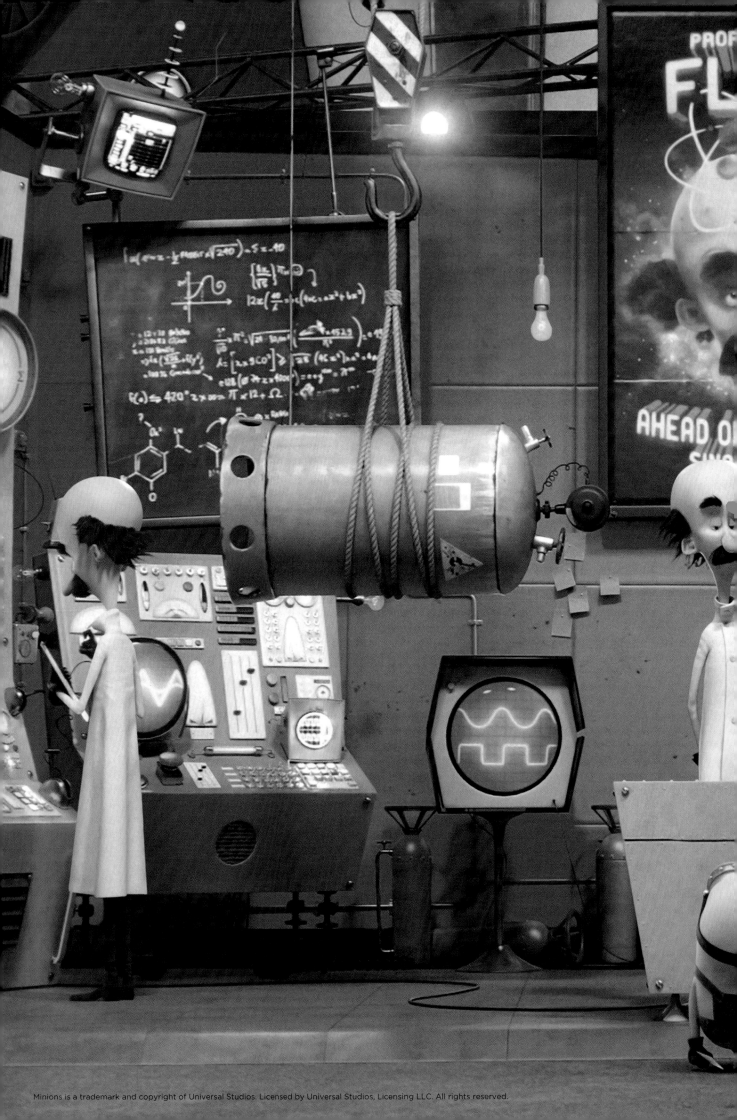

Where's the flag?

**What's this?! Minion pirates without a flag?
Oh, no, no, no, NO! This will never do.**

Help these Minions find their flag without getting them eaten by a hungry shark. If they DO get eaten by a hungry shark, you can skip the flag part.

FINISH

↑ START

HOW DID YOU DO?
Check your answer
on page 55.

13

MASTERS THROUGH HISTORY:
NAPOLEON BONAPARTE

Ah Napoleon – short, power crazy and fond of conquering countries.

The Minions thought they'd found their perfect master fit, at last. But all too soon the dream was over, and the Minions found themselves out in the cold.

MASTER PROS:

- Leader of France
- Exciting travel opportunities
- A real emperor

MASTER FAIL:

- Napoleon (and his army) didn't appreciate 'blow up the leader'!

DID YOU KNOW?
- Napoleon's nickname was **Little Commander**.
- After being exiled on an island he escaped and took over Paris again.
- He once wrote a romance novel.

VIVE LE MINION

Minions like having their portraits painted just as much as Napoleon Bonaparte himself.

Use your pens to colour this picture – or it's to the guillotine with you!

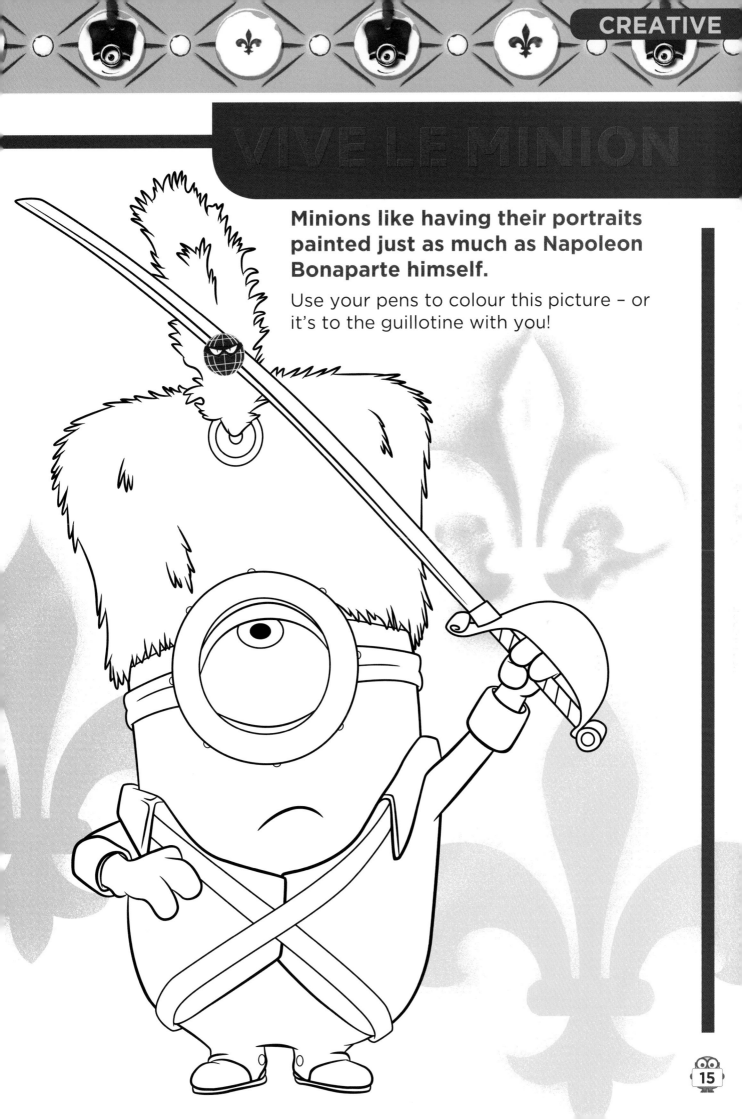

MASTERS FROM THE PAST

How much did you learn about the Minions' past masters?

Take this true or false quiz to find out.

1

T. rex's name means 'tyrant master'.

True or **False**

2

T. rex lived 7 million years ago.

True or **False**

3

Cavemen made paintings on the inside of caves.

True or **False**

4

Homo sapien means 'knowing man'.

True or **False**

5

Ancient Egyptians called their kings or queens 'pharaohs'

True or **False**

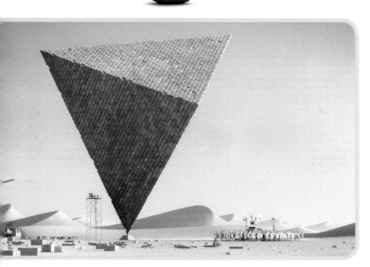

6

A pyramid is a type of tomb.

True or **False**

7

Dracula's name means 'son of the bat'.

True or **False**

8

Vampires cannot go out in sunlight.

True or **False**

9

Pirates pierced their ears to help eyesight.

True or **False**

10

Pirates used compasses to navigate.

True or **False**

11

Napoleon's nickname was 'Minion commander'.

True or **False**

12

Napoleon was the ruler of Italy.

True or **False**

How hard were you studying the Minions' past masters? Check your answers to find out:

1-5 Must try harder. You need to do better to impress your big boss!

5-7 OK. You're becoming more yellow before my eyes!

7-12 You're ready! You know all there is to know about masters of the past. Now help Kevin, Stuart and Bob journey to Villain-Con and use what they've learnt to seek out the ultimate master!

HOW DID YOU DO?
Check your answers on page 55.

THROUGH THE KEYHOLE

Looking through keyholes is sometimes an essential part of a villain's job. It's not big, it's not pretty, but sometimes it has to be done!

Look through these keyholes and match what you can see to the correct images.

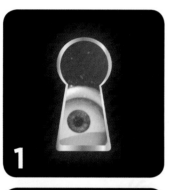
1

2

3

4

5

ONE IMAGE ISN'T BEHIND ANY OF THE KEYHOLES, which is it?

A

B

C

D

E

F

HOW DID YOU DO? Check your answers on page 56.

18

MINION MUDDLE

Being part of a tribe means it's very easy to get tangled up! Just look at this Minion muddle!

Carefully count how many Minions you can see in all this mess.

THERE ARE THREE VILLAINS HIDING IN THE PICTURE, TOO. Who are they?

MINIONS THROUGH TIME

Minions have been serving different masters a VERY long time. In fact it's been so long that sometimes it's good to sit down and have a recap.

Help these Minions find where they belong in history, by adding the stickers and drawing lines from them to where they belong on the timeline.

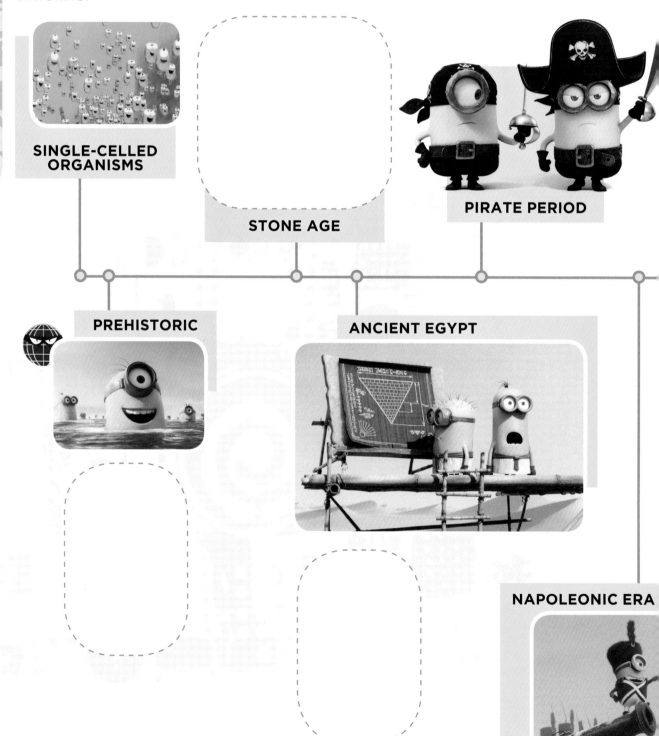

SINGLE-CELLED ORGANISMS

STONE AGE

PIRATE PERIOD

PREHISTORIC

ANCIENT EGYPT

NAPOLEONIC ERA

VILLAIN-CON

ICE CAVE

1960s NEW YORK

1960s LONDON

WHEN'S YOUR PERFECT PERIOD IN HISTORY?

Doodle yourself on the timeline in your favourite era.

KEN KEN

Every villain needs to keep their smarts up when they're planning a heist.

Test you've got what it takes by solving this kerfuffling Ken Ken puzzle. Use the numbers 1, 2 and 3 to fill in the boxes below. Do not repeat any number in a row or a column. Make sure numbers in the same area add up to the number shown in the top left corner of each cage.

WHICH NUMBER IS IN THE YELLOW BOX?

HOW DID YOU DO?
Check your answers on page 56.

VILLAIN CON HALL OF FAME

Can you match these four famous faces from Villain-Con to their descriptions below?

When you know who's who, find their sticker and place it beneath each description.

1
- I have brown hair
- I invented the Far-Out Stretch Suit
- I'm pretty groovy!

2
- I am not human
- I love my teddy bear, Tim
- My eyes are two different colours

3
- I have a quick temper
- I love the Royals
- My favourite colour is red

4
- I love to rob banks
- I have three children
- My name begins with W

MATCH THESE MINIONS TO THE CORRECT MASTER.

IT'S TIME FOR
ANSWERS

PAGE 3
1. BANANA! 2. BLUMOCK 3. POTAKINO LO PATATA 4. BIG BOSS 5. BELLO

PAGE 5

PAGE 7
1.C; 2.A; 3.B

PAGE 9

PAGE 11

PAGE 13

PAGE 16 & 17
1. False. It means 'tyrant lizard'.
2. False. It was 70 million years ago!
3. True 4. True 5. True
6. True 7. False. It means 'son of the dragon'. 8. True 9. True 10. True
11. False. It was 'little commander'.
12. False. He was the ruler of France.

PAGE 18
1.C; 2.E; 3.A; 4.F; 5.B
Image D isn't behind any of the keyholes.

PAGE 19
17 Minions
Scarlet, Napoleon and T. rex

PAGE 22
The number 2 goes in the yellow box.

DID YOU FIND THE VILLAIN-CON LOGO HIDDEN ON EVERY PAGE?